DREAM FOREVER

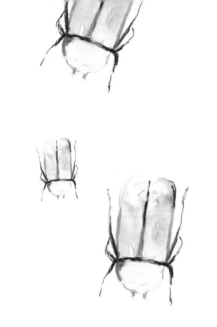

DREAMS COME TO LIFE WITH ACTION.

"A PERSON IS THE PRODUCT OF THEIR DREAMS. SO MAKE SURE TO DREAM GREAT DREAMS. AND THEN TRY TO LIVE YOUR DREAM."

- MAYA ANGELOU

WOULDN'T TAKE NOTHING FOR MY JOURNEY NOW

DREAM BIG!

What's a tree
to its branch!?

What's a branch
to its twig!?

What's a twig
to a baby bug, nesting
with its mom trying to
get snug!?

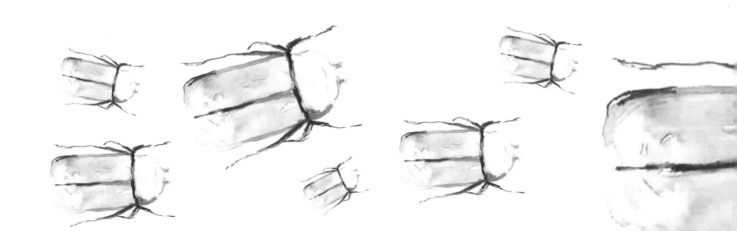

What's a baby
bug's **DREAM**!?
Do they get
from life what it
seems!?
Do they **DREAM** of
climbing trees!?

2

Do they DREAM of being the sun that beams!?

I'm sure I don't know,
but I would tell that
baby bug to **DREAM**
a **DREAM** so **BIG** that
when they catch it,
they glow.

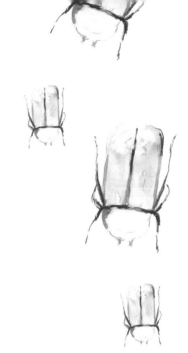

DREAM BIG!

DREAM bigger than you are.

DREAM bigger than your fears.

DREAM DREAM so **BIG**
that when they come true you cry tears.

Cry those tears of joy.
No matter if you are a girl or a boy.

6

DREAM bigger
and **DREAM** more!

Bigger than any moon.

Bigger than any chore.

Bigger than any tune.

Bigger than
any item
from a store.

8

DREAM
of where you came.

DREAM
of where you're going.

DREAM
beyond your aim.

DREAM
beyond your knowing.

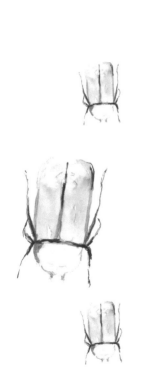

DREAM
of cool things.

DREAM
of new things.

DREAM
of things that aren't things.

Dream of doing a good deed.
Dream of planting a seed.

DREAM
of a good feeling.

DREAM
of all the pain healing.

DREAM
of love unfurled.

DREAM
of a peaceful world.

14

Trust in your dreams, they
know more than you.
With belief and faith
your **DREAMS** will come true.

Just like your parents **DREAMED** of you.

FOREVER

THE END.

CPSIA information can be obtained
at www.ICGtesting.com
Printed in the USA
LVHW072341021220
673228LV00014B/626

* 9 7 8 0 6 9 2 9 2 7 0 5 2 *